EXPOSIT

Hele

First published 9th September 2022 by Fly on the Wall Press
Published in the UK by
Fly on the Wall Press
56 High Lea Rd
New Mills
Derbyshire
SK22 3DP

www.flyonthewallpress.co.uk
ISBN:9781913211882

Typesetting by Isabelle Kenyon. Cover photo- Shutterstock .

A CIP Catalogue record for this book is available from the British Library.

Dedication

Thank you to Angela Cleland, for the prompt which started this whole thing, and to Gill and Pia for their encouragement when the very first exposition lady was just a scrappy workshop draft.

Thank you to Simon, for his endless patience while I shouted 'Exposition Lady!' at least once during every film we watched in 2021.

Exposition Ladies is dedicated in loving memory to Linda Mugadzaweta, who taught me so much about fiction, feminism and finding a voice.

Contents:

The Reservoir

I am the exposition lady, picking up the phone as I shout in too much detail, as I hang from a window for better signal, a clearer message, within earshot of the handsome man who will claim credit for knowledge gleaned from my call, as I explain, in still too much detail, to the men, the men on the end of the phone and the men on the street and the men in the thick of it and the men in the audience, that my best guess is that one in five people who drank the infected water will in fact drop dead, and yes, their festering corpses will become toxic, but no, the science has not yet confirmed that their toxicity will be airborne so please, just hold tight and definitely don't drink the water, and no, don't touch the bodies, and no, why would you do that anyway, and yes, what we really need is a hero, but no, we don't know where to find one, and dammit, where are all the heroes when we need them, someone bold and brave with medical training and a hazmat suit and rippling abs—under the hazmat suit—and hair that doesn't move, someone unflappable, needs to come and put a stop to this, and dammit, they need to get to the reservoir quick, they need to cut of the city's water supply and then, my phone will *beep, beep, beep*, the battery will run low, and I will sigh, and I cannot use my knowledge to save the world because I am but a woman, on a phone, providing exposition, and I will never get credit for saving your arses, but for god's sake, if nothing else, please just get to the reservoir.

Stage Three

I am the exposition lady and oh hey girl! Sorry I'm late it's been a nightmare day! Oh, yes, just a flat white for me please... Where were we? How's it going since that meeting with your boss where he didn't listen to your ideas? And your landlord put the rent up? And your dad called to say that your mom isn't feeling so great? I bet he would really appreciate an extra pair of hands, at the orchard! Is apple season, back home? How did Brad take that, after eight dates was it, or nine? Did he even say he would miss you? Is he still saying he wants to take it slow? Can you afford to take it slow? You always said that you love the life your mom lived? The big family! The orchard! You never meant the city to be your forever home!

~~Me? Sure I'm fine too I guess, the test results are back, they said it's reached stage three, and I haven't told the kids but that's enough about my problems, as they'll never come up again, and I am an exposition friend, a half-formed vessel, a backstory for your forward trajectory...~~

We're here to talk about you! And the orchard! And Brad! And your boss! And you have *so* much going on, go back to the orchard and harvest your true love, girl!

Underdogs

I am the exposition lady and this, ladies, is your big moment. This is your time to shine, the first time I—*we*—have made regionals in 17 years, the last time I—*we*—did this was when I was captain, and now here I am as coach.

Don't let me—*yourselves*—down, ladies, this is my time, your time, our time, it is an honour and a privilege to coach you, it is a glimmer of hope that I have not been wasting my life. Confirmation that I was correct to let true love go and stay here and coach rugby while Jeanne and Bianca moved to Bordeaux and bought a vineyard and raised hens.

Because now the game is my true love and you have one chance to make this all worth it, for me, for yourselves, and ladies—after the scandal with the boys' team I want to remind you that if you can't join them, beat them.

We will always be the underdogs and they will always call us bitches but our bite is worse than their bark so go out there and win this, yourselves! For everyone who ever doubted you, or called you names, or said you couldn't do it.

And for me, it's been 17 years. For me, go underdogs. For me.

Camp Counsellors

I am the exposition lady, and I guess you've like, heard the rumours, but like, don't worry, the camp isn't really haunted, it's just like, an urban legend, about the counsellor who like, died, after like, swimming in the lake, after drinking from the hipflask, that like, the camp leader gave her, after one too many strokes, and by strokes, I mean, you know... and like, anyway, that was the 90s, and sure, the owners haven't changed, but like, it's been such a long time, and they say she only comes, if you play the Backstreet Boys, so you really shouldn't worry, even though this was her room, you know? And anyway, like the radio's right there, so that can drown out all your fears, and like I say, it's just a rumours, so it really is okay, so like, just crank up the volume and

♫♫♫ *I want it that way...* ♫♫♫

Mother's Place

I am the exposition lady, here to say thanks to you both for coming to this meeting, to talk about how your daughter has been acting out since the separation.

Listen, I'm sure it's hard when you both have such high-flying jobs, and you're probably asking yourselves how would I, a lowly school teacher, the only person who ever listens to your damn daughter, could ever understand how tough it is at the top.

Look, your child needs stability, she's unsettled and disruptive, and soon she'll fall behind, and I know it's not my business but surely someone has to care, not that I think that you don't.

Understand, though, a daughter needs her mother, and a family needs two parents, so if you could think about your priorities then perhaps things will get better and it really is important to set a good example.

So, how can you be there for her when you're always out at work, and like I say, it's not my business, but I hope you two can sort it out.

Spilt Milk

I am the exposition lady,

in a crime thriller,

trauma porn,

someone else's

dark fantasy,

and so I open

my fridge, in the

dark of the night,

and the crack

of light reveals

a shadow, before

I am dragged

kicking

and

screaming

from my house,

and all I wanted

was a glass of milk

from the fridge

in a heavy-handed

metaphor for

fertility and frigidity

and you really better

catch this guy or my

pain

has

been

for

nothing.

Festival Season

I am the exposition lady, and I don't think you're from around here.

It seems like you have questions, but there's nothing going on.

I'm trying to teach a class, so please don't disturb the girls.

We can step outside, if you must go around in circles.

Perhaps I've seen that picture, but it's been a long, long time.

People come and go, I don't think that that's a crime.

Now I really can't say more, you will see that we're quite busy.

Will you be joining us for highsun noontime festival season?

Why is it that you came here? You've not given a reason.

Will we see you at the feast?

Will we have you here for dinner?

It's a big day in our culture.

We will sort the sinned from sinners.

Vaseline

I am the exposition lady; in soft focus I undress while listening to Max Richter on vinyl; I eat a pastry in my underwear; I stretch, pull back the curtains; I am carefree; a perfume advert; a *Vaseline* lens to a teenage dream; my cheekbones will break your heart and the cinematography will win awards; for the next two hours, nothing much will happen.

Cliques

I am the exposition lady, welcome to our high school, I'm sure you'll fit in, we have lots of cliques to choose from, from thinly-veiled machismo, through to stereotypes of stoners, and the grungies and the grebos who give away the ages of the writers, and the girls who are sexually active, who are painted a problem, and the boys who they are sleeping with, who are shown as heros, and the dubious racial profiles, and the clichés and the looks, but stick with us and you'll be fine, just change the way you are—honestly you do seem great, but we can make you better, so stick with us you'll be just fine as long as we're together, and I haven't asked a question and I don't suppose I will, as your eyes drift to a table of people who aren't cool, and sure there might be tension, and you might be hard to crack but welcome to our high school, let's hope someone has your back.

PC Other

I am the exposition lady, working at the shop, not much goes on in town here so it's fun to meet a cop. It all started by the river, when they found the washed-up shoes, which I think looked like Betty's but she swears that I'm confused.

So anyway, that day was frosty, I remember well, and the shop was drafty… But this lad you're looking for, what's his deal? I always trust my instincts, see, I always go by feel, and I saw a lad, the one you want, looked about five foot ten. I'll tell you when I saw him, I had a shiver down my spine.

But sorry no I do digress, I hope the toerag will confess. I didn't like his hoodie see, or the way he looked at me. He might have gone towards the river, but really I was all a-quiver. I don't like getting incomers, they scare away the customers. I hope that you'll look into him, even if he's not the crim.

Remind me what your question was? You need to know about the village coz, without the context you're on your own, so for more exposition, any time now, please just phone.

Breaking

I am the exposition lady
I studied law at Magdalene
College, Oxford, before an
internship with The Telegraph
and a journalism qualification
at King's College London, and I
bring you this news, to give you
exposition, and expertise, on a
growing political development
in the Middle East, which requires
nuance, diplomacy, and for god's
sake understanding, but which will
from here on out, be addressed by
men, in rooms, without enough chairs
pacing, and leaning, against walls
covered in maps, without any nod
to the political origins or cartography
or colonial nationhood, who will
create hard-hitting one-liners and
fix problems with brute force and
brooding looks while I produce
this exposition and then, finally,
cut to a segment about a badger

rescuing an old lady from a post office in Swanage

Extremely Cursed

I am the exposition lady and I will visit you
in a dream to let you know about a curse
set about by the ancients, a curse so dark and so disturbing

your blood
will curdle
your skin
will crawl

a curse from the ancients, so vague and so variable that it could
be anything
at any time
so you will ignore the warnings I offer as the madness
of a simple crone
a haunted witch
an invisible
older woman

Until one day it is too late, and you search your mind for details, and you search the room for clues and your girlfriend, precious girlfriend, is screaming as she packs, as she reminds you of the words, and her face contorts to mine, and still you do not listen to your girl, your beautiful girl, your now ex girl, your final girl, who will live on in the words of advice I died to bring you, and which you did not hear.

Today's Special

I am the exposition lady, here to wait your table. I will make it known that this is a nice place, that we have certain standards which must be upheld, though of course I'll find it charming when you disregard our etiquette. I will laugh politely, while you show instead of tell just how important you all are. I will look coquettish, but jealous, as we aspire to a dream in which cash is king and I serve your every whim. I will be a diligent, demure reminder to the onlookers that rules really don't apply, while you will be the dirty, debauched reminder to the staff that we're barely getting by. Another bottle of Moet? Another round of shots? When I serve you this at breakfast, just imagine the third act, where you've had it all and lost it too, raining down fat stacks, and until then just keep going, a prop to show your wealth, the whisky and the women, just here for exposition, never for myself.

Analogue

I am the exposition lady, background noise, a cracking radio, a dire warning or an overreaction, as I tell you, gravely, of another teenager struck down by a mysterious, and seemingly deadly, internet craze, a craze lost in the crackling of the FM and carried by the waves, as my voice returns, to say something is sweeping the nation, something was posted to TikTok, but the tuning isn't right, and there's weather interference so you only half hear when I tell you that, in all of my years, I have never seen any evidence for this phenomenon, and between the white noise crackles, I say that yes, I've heard the stories about the superhuman teenagers who go on to age at over 100 times their usual rate, and are dying of conditions and symptoms usually associated with old age, mere hours or days after undertaking daring acts; but that this sounds like an urban legend, and there is no doubt a sensible, scientific explanation—but the radio cuts out before you ever hear my answer, and I am the exposition lady, crackling into the void.

Right On Right On

I am the exposition lady.

retro outfit,

short

short

shorts,

big hair, big placard

'MY BODY MY CHOICE',

a car rolls past I shout

about

human rights,

through a window a man in a suit will wink,

I will smile, and I will blush,

as love and hate

good and evil

define me in multitudes,

but first,

let's make some noise,

make some change,

come on girls,

fuck the system,

fuck the man, then fuck a man

cum, on, girl,

a feel-good film, about hard won rights,

choices about bodies front and centre,

my body, your body, don't tell anybody,

to the man in the car, my body, my choice,

my body, his choice, my body,

my body, look at my body.

Hitching Up

I am the exposition lady, standing at the side of the road in the pouring rain, trying to make a call, trying to get signal, trying to use an umbrella in gale-force wind while cars speed by and puddles splash, as the rain bleeds through my shirt and my god it's cold and I am miles from anywhere, I'm just trying to make a call, against a panning shot of country roads and speeding cars, and Jesus, would you pick up the phone, my nipples could cut glass over here, and oh—oh—a single bar of signal and I shout down the phone, for fuck's sake come and get me, the car broke down, it's getting dark, I'm fucking freezing and—the A2214—I don't fucking know, near the trees, where they found the bodies—come and get me, I'm all alone and miles from anything, oh forget it, I— HANG ON, HANG ON, STOP, PLEASE—don't worry about it there's a car slowing down, I'll be fine, I am the exposition woman, hitching through the woods, and my nipples could cut men over here.

Sorry, Alison

I am the exposition woman.

Talking to another woman.

Self-aware.

The Bechdel test—

when a film has two women

who have names

and speak to each other

about something other than a man.

I am the exposition woman, oh sorry, call me Jane, telling you, let's call you Amanda, that it is only a matter of time until the professor gets caught out, and if we stand together we can take him down, I've spoken to dozens of girls like you, girls who are unique and special and just young enough to titillate a viewer in a film about a creepy old professor, who isn't Woody Allen, but a Woody Allen type, and think about your column, or your manuscript or play, and how we suffer for our art, so just come, speak up, okay?

I know they'll say you're lying, or that he's misunderstood, but when we work together we can take him down for good, so we'll all meet at the dorms and be serious but cute, and I am the exposition woman, and this film is so #metoo.

Laced

I am the exposition lady.
My panties stuffed
into my cold dead
mouth in the opening
shot.
A warning.
A welcome.
A film that hates women.

About the Author

Helen Bowie (they/she) is a writer, performer and feminist killjoy. They have created interactive and playable comedy on themes including the housing crisis and capitalist patriarchy for festivals such as Wilderness, Emergency and the Camden Fringe. Her first poetry pamphlet, WORD/PLAY was released by Beir Bua Press in July 2021, and her poetry has been longlisted and shortlisted for various prizes. Helen has written about representations of gender, class and queer identities for publications including Screen Queens, StarTrek.com and Eater.

About Fly on the Wall Press

A publisher with a conscience.
Publishing high quality anthologies, novels, short stories and poetry on pressing issues, from exceptional writers around the globe. Founded in 2018 by founding editor, Isabelle Kenyon.

Some other publications:

The Woman With An Owl Tattoo by Anne Walsh Donnelly
The Prettyboys of Gangster Town by Martin Grey
The Sound of the Earth Singing to Herself by Ricky Ray
Inherent by Lucia Orellana Damacela
Medusa Retold by Sarah Wallis
Pigskin by David Hartley
We Are All Somebody
Aftereffects by Jiye Lee
Someone Is Missing Me by Tina Tamsho-Thomas
*Odd as F*ck by Anne Walsh Donnelly*
Muscle and Mouth by Louise Finnigan
These Mothers of Gods by Rachel Bower
Sin Is Due To Open In A Room Above Kitty's by Morag Anderson
Fauna by David Hartley
How To Bring Him Back by Clare HM
Hassan's Zoo and A Village in Winter by Ruth Brandt
No One Has Any Intention of Building A Wall by Ruth Brandt
Snapshots of the Apocalypse by Katy Wimhurst
Man at Sea by Liam Bell

Social Media:

@fly_press (Twitter) @flyonthewall_poetry (Instagram)

@flyonthewallpress (Facebook) www.flyonthewallpress.co.uk